Thin Black Lines RIDES AGAIN

~ political cartoons and development education

written and compiled by
Colm Regan, Scott Sinclair, Martyn Turner

Published by
Development Education Centre [Birmingham]
in association with
Cartoonists & Writers Syndicate, New York

Copies available from:
Development Education Centre
998 Bristol Road
Selly Oak
Birmingham B29 6LE, UK.

ISBN: 0 948838 30 2

Six years ago we published **Thin Black Lines** to encourage the use of cartoons in education. We felt that political cartoons presented complex and challenging ideas about important world issues in an accessible and usable way.

Judging by the success of **Thin Black Lines** and by the wide use of the cartoons from it, many of you agree with us about the value of cartoons. This has prompted us to produce **Thin Black Lines Rides Again**. We hope you like it. We've organised the book around four central themes which we feel have broad application and relevance.

We still feel, however, that the value of cartoons in education is under-developed and so we have again included a range of activities to make good use of them. From time to time throughout the book we have also included questions to help focus discussion around the cartoons.

We are particularly pleased to present in the introduction the words and works of Ollie Harrington who is an extraordinary cartoonist.

Thin Black Lines Rides Again is published by the Development Education Centre, Birmingham in association with the Cartoonists & Writers Syndicate in New York. We are especially pleased with this partnership, and sincerely thank Jerry and Jens Robinson of C & W for their enthusiastic support and co-operation. Finally, we would like to thank all those cartoonists whose collective brains and hands have made us all more aware, forewarned [and terrified!]. Thanks.

Contents

Introduction   **4**

Ollie Harrington - portrait of a political cartoonist   **8**

The shape of the world   **15**

Human Rights   **21**
"The issue is not whether torture is more important than starvation
. . . human rights are universal and indivisible"
Pierre Sane, Secretary General, Amnesty International

- *Values . . . the right to imagine*   22
- *And all are treated equally*   26
- *Africa . . . the right to life denied*   31
- *Responsibility . . . pointing a finger?*   37

Environment   **43**
". . . and on the seventh day we took over"

- *In words . . . and deeds?*   44
- *Not even the trees . . . ?*   50
- *. . . Nor the sea . . . ?*   52
- *Nor the air?*   55
- *Now we know . . . or do we?*   60

The end of an era   **63**
"at stake . . . is something more than war over words; the battle lines
are drawn between conflicting interpretations of reality . . . the first
values efficiency and social control, the second social justice . . ."
Denis Goulet, philosopher

- *New world order . . . out of order*   64
- *Economics . . . signs of the times*   69
- *Debt . . . paying with their lives?*   77
- *Arms . . . winners . . . and losers*   80
- *Conflict . . . war no more?*   84
- *The future UN role . . . a UNited future?*   92

Index and Acknowledgements   **99**

Using political cartoons in development education

Political cartoons can be a particularly valuable resource for development education. At their best they encapsulate some very complex issues, different viewpoints, and some of the contradictions which are a real part of many situations. Political cartoons do not simply take sides, they offer a challenge to us all. They can make links between issues which sometimes turn things inside out. They don't spare our sensitivities - this is their essential strength.

Political cartoons will often provide the stimulus to stop and think, to look sideways or look afresh at a particular issue. We hope that readers of this book will find much to provide a focus for personal reflection. However, the main purpose of this section is to outline a few basic activities for the use of cartoons in group discussion.

A word of warning may be useful here. If you see education in general, or development education in particular, as a process of endorsing certain "acceptable" ideas or viewpoints and rejecting others, rather than as a means of exploring, discussing and debating ideas and opinions as a way of encouraging people to make up their own minds, then don't use cartoons. It is unlikely that they will provide enough opportunity for control!

Cartoons have a number of advantages as a stimulus to group discussion. They often contain a lot of information, yet can be assimilated quite quickly. It is possible for people with a range of knowledge of the issues [or none at all] to respond to the same stimulus, and for the discussion to reflect different levels of experience. The humour of cartoons also contributes to the group's interactions. Laughter is important, but this humour can also disarm us of our assumptions and help us look afresh at the issues. Many of the cartoons you might choose to use as a stimulus will be quite explicit in the main issues they bring to the group's agenda, they are, however, at the same time very open ended. They provide the opportunity for a group to explore the aspects they see as most important or most at issue.

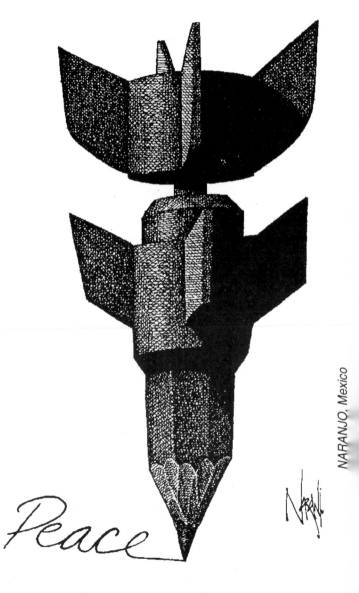

NARANJO, Mexico

Peace

LANGER, Argentina

Some basic activities.......

The activities outlined here can be adapted to a wide range of learning situations. It is, however, important to note that we need to build up skills in using cartoons as stimulus material.

The learning skills that can be developed by using material such as cartoons include:

- making careful observations;

- acquiring information from the cartoon;

- analysing and evaluating information;

- relating one's own views to those in the cartoons;

- recognising the value of different interpretations;

- empathising with the people/situations portrayed;

- forming links between the ideas in different cartoons.

There is a sense in which cartoons can help us to laugh at ourselves and our involvement, individually and as a society, in fairly desperate situations. Perhaps we should identify this as a skill too.

NARANJO, Mexico

Thin Black Lines Rides Again has three main sections, each made up of smaller collections of cartoons based on a theme. They could be used using the themes we have chosen, or by making your own selection from different parts of the book. Either way it is worth adding cartoons you collect from newspapers about recent events.

The following are some ideas which could be used with any collection of cartoons.

Warming up

What does it say to you?

You could ask this question of any cartoon, but there is special value in asking it about one which is open to very wide interpretation.

The discussion will move quite rapidly away from the cartoon to the interests and concerns of the members of the group. This kind of activity is particularly valuable when you are trying to work with a new group, or when people in the group don't know each other very well. A reasonable amount of time should be allowed for people to work on their initial thoughts and to share ideas.

Reading a cartoon.....

It may be useful to take time to discuss one or two cartoons and work on "reading" them.

Ask small groups to look closely at the details:

- *what is the cartoon saying?*
- *what different interpretations do they imagine could be made?*
- *what symbols are used?*
- *who are the characters?*
- *what is suggested about the context of the cartoon?*

Bring the groups together to share their discussion, but steer the discussion away from the issues and focus on **how** they read the cartoons.

What's the theme? What are the issues?

When you introduce a theme to a group it is useful to find ways to explore what they already know about it. Display a collection of cartoons [say ten] and ask the group to look at them. Working in pairs decide what main theme[s] link them as a collection. Each pair could then choose a number of cartoons [say three] which highlight the main issues as they see them, and make them into a poster to be shared with the rest of the group.

Sharing views

Another useful way to introduce a collection of cartoons is to ask people to choose from those on display three cartoons which they like most ... or which say most to them about the issues being considered. They could mark these with a sticker with their name on and then pair up with someone who has chosen the same cartoons to discuss their choice. *Are the reasons the same? Did they see different things in the same cartoon?*

This activity also has the advantage of mixing the group, reviewing the whole collection and looking at some cartoons more closely. The pairs can share the highlights of their discussion and introduce one of the cartoons they chose to the rest of the group.

Questioning and asking questions

This can be used as an introductory activity leading to an 'agenda' of things to do further work on, or as a way of focusing on one or two cartoons to make a more detailed study of them.

Give each pair a copy of a cartoon mounted on a large sheet of paper and ask them to write around the edge, as many questions as they can relating to the cartoon. This encourages a close look at detail as well as at the cartoon as a whole. It is not necessary to be able to answer the questions; the process of asking them will provide a good stimulus to the discussion when the pair share their work with other groups.

Another approach which would encourage more detailed study of one cartoon is for you to pose the questions for the group to consider. This can help focus on the detailed context of a particular situation and encourage insight into the ways in which symbolism is used by cartoonists.

Headlining ... changing the context

Ask pairs to choose a cartoon around which they then develop a headline and/or short article. *If they use different headlines does it influence how the cartoon comes over?*

The pairs could then share their article with the rest of the group. It may be useful to choose different cartoons and therefore raise a wide range of issues, or you might choose the same one and explore the different ways in which it is viewed.

Ranking

This is a very effective activity to encourage groups to consider a small collection of cartoons [say nine] in detail. Give each group nine cartoons and ask them to order them from those they feel raise the most important issues to those that raise the least important. Alternatively you could ask pairs to rank the cartoons in terms of those they like most/ least.

Ranking can enable a full discussion because the task makes sure everyone has been involved in thinking about the issues and then highlighting the main points to share with other groups.

An issue agenda

Cartoons can be a very useful stimulus for motivating a group to plan further work. This gives an opportunity to find out more about the starting points in a group - the assumptions and understanding individuals bring to new areas of work.

Using a collection of cartoons on a particular theme you could ask questions such as:

- *What issues do they refer to?*
- *How do they reflect different approaches to issues such as development, environment, peace?*
- *Who might disagree with the views of the cartoonists? Why?*

Questions such as these make a useful start to building up an agenda. It is also vital to ask about other relevant issues not shown in the cartoons. The discussion could then be focused by suggesting that each group draws up a list of questions about the issues which need to be followed up.

Ollie Harrington
portrait of a political cartoonist

Oliver Wendell Harrington was born in Valhalla, New York, on Valentine's Day in 1912. His father, Herbert, was an escaped slave from North Carolina, and his mother, Eugenia, was a Jewish music student originally from Hungary.

"In America, are the most creatively inventive technically developed, prolific cartoonists in the world today. At least that is my own unbiased opinion. Their mastery did not come about as a gift from heaven, or even from the benediction of high ranking politicians though you may some times be given that impression. The truth of the matter is that this comes about as a result of certain time-proven natural laws which indicate that when human beings of many different cultures and experiences are joined together in one society, the result is a more creative and more productive society.

This is recognised, rather superficially I am afraid, when one talks about the great American melting pot. Irish Americans, Greek Americans German, Lithuanian, French and Polish Ameri cans are part of the mix, but African Americans can forget about it.

Fortunately for my own mental health, I worked a kind of self therapy while I tried to open the doors of countless art editors where the words NO BLACKS ALLOWED were hanging. For about 60 years I have been locked out, black balled Jim Crowed, or whatever terminology is cur rently fashionable. All of the terms simply mean that the American cartoon industry shut its doors on me with a bang."

"An we're gonna clean up this country . . . startin' wit' you!"

"Hey, I hear that the cops been ordered not to shoot up us black kids 'till AFTER the Olympics!"

Ollie Harrington attended an unsegregated school in the South Bronx, where a racist schoolteacher was responsible for starting his career as a cartoonist.

"Our teacher was a Miss McCoy, a tall, pasty faced vixen who seemed to have devoted all her attention to her weird hair-do. I always felt oddly apprehensive in her presence, watchful and alert. Was this the birth of intuition? I have heard it said in similar circumstances that it was probably paranoia. All I can say to that is - in the case of black folks - thank god for paranoia.

One bright morning Miss McCoy ordered us - the two black kids - to the front of class. Pausing for several seconds, she pointed her cheaply jewelled finger [with what I think she considered a very dramatic gesture] at the trash basket and said, 'Never, never forget. These two belong in that trash basket.' The white kids giggled rather hesitantly and then fell about in peals of laughter. For those kids it must have been their first trip on the racist drug.

I stumbled backwards in shocked resentment, aware of the growing pain in my chest. The other kid only grinned, but I noticed that his eyes had suddenly narrowed. It was several days before I managed to pull myself together. Gradually I felt the urge to draw little caricatures of Miss McCoy in the margins of my notebook; Miss McCoy being rammed into our local butcher's meat grinding apparatus; Miss McCoy being run over by the speeding engines on the nearby New York Central Railroad tracks. One, which I worked all through arithmetic class, really grabbed me. It showed Miss McCoy disappearing between the jaws of a particularly enthusiastic tiger. I began to realise that each drawing lifted my wounded spirits a bit higher. I did little sketches of the people around me, not from life as I learned to do in art class, but from memory. Miss McCoy never caught me at it, but I began to dream of being a cartoonist."

After he finished high school, Ollie Harrington discovered Harlem and met many of the leading figures of the Harlem Renaissance. In 1933 he began his chronicle of the life of an ordinary man living in Harlem. He claimed "*not much imagination was needed for the job. I simply recorded the almost unbelievable but hilarious chaos around me and came up with a character.*" This character was Bootsie. He featured in a cartoon panel that eventually appeared in the **Amsterdam News**, the **Baltimore Afro-American**, and the **Pittsburgh Courier**. During the thirty years he drew Bootsie, Ollie Harrington used the cartoon to reflect the lives and concerns of "ordinary" African Americans.

Although many of the *Bootsie* cartoons were funny, humour was not an end in itself. Ollie Harrington's work may be described as a social documentary. He observed life, recording details of speech, dress and activity in the African American community. Because he was not an outsider making these observations, Harrington's *Bootsie* has unique credibility. Given the longevity and popularity of the feature, its readers must have enjoyed the mirror of their lives provided by these cartoons.

"Annual Marathon, Man are you kiddin'? These folks are answerin' a newspaper ad for a coupl'a job openings downtown!"

NEWS ITEM: Postal authorities in line with the President's "WINNABLE NUCLEAR WAR" theory assured the public that mail deliveries would be maintained regardless of prevailing conditions.

Ollie Harrington studied at the National Academy of Design and graduated from Yale in 1939 with a bachelor of fine arts degree. During World War II he served as a war correspondent for **Pittsburgh Courier** in North Africa and Europe. After his discharge, he had a variety of jobs - journalist, cartoonist, book illustrator and baseball outfielder - until he became director of public relations for the National Association for the Advancement of Colored People in 1948.

He was angry and appalled at the treatment of African American veterans of World War II by the country which they had defended. In his NAACP position, he worked diligently in the South long before sit-ins publicised the need for justice for minorities there. Because of his outspoken efforts, opponents began to label him as a Communist. In 1951 he was warned by a friend who was an Army Intelligence agent that for his own safety, he should leave the country. Because he was concerned about the future of the NAACP as well as his own safety, three weeks later he was bound for Europe. Except for a two week trip to the US in 1972, he did not return to his homeland again until he was honoured with an exhibition at the Museum of African American History in Detroit in 1991.

Paris was a welcoming city for American expatriates in the 1950's and Ollie Harrington enjoyed a wide community of friends and continued to paint and draw *Bootsie*. He travelled to Berlin in 1961 to meet with publishers interested in having him illustrate a series of books reprinting classic American literature. While he was there, the Berlin Wall was erected and, since he lacked the proper visas, he was unable to leave East Berlin.

He lost everything for the second time in his life and he responded to this challenge by beginning a new existence. After his American contracts for *Bootsie* were terminated in 1963, he found new outlets for his work in several magazines, especially *Eulenspiegel*, and in the **People's Daily World**, a New York City tabloid. Harrington's pen and brush have been described as 'weapons of combat' as he reframed and enlarged the targets for his wit. For the first time, he was able to work in colour which added yet another dimension to his ability to express himself. On the personal level, he married Helma Richter, an economist, and they had a son, Oliver Jr.

The unification of Germany and the end of the Cold War brought yet another dimension to Ollie Harrington's life. He can visit his homeland freely and has expressed his hope that his son will some day attend an American university.

Some critics have characterised cartoon art as ephemeral, a lesser form of art than painting or sculpture. Ollie Harrington's work cannot be dismissed so easily. His cartoons reflect their times from the viewpoint of an unusually talented and perceptive man. His own experiences, tempered with resilience and determination, provide a remarkable lens through which he views the world. Humour and outrage blend to challenge those who see his cartoons.

This piece has been adapted from a speech given by Ollie Harrington at the Ohio State University's Festival of Cartoon Art in 1992, and from Professor Lucy Shelton Caswell's biographical sketch from **Cartoons and Ethnicity**.

Many thanks to OSU for permission to use the texts and from Ollie Harrington for permission to reprint the cartoons. Oliver Harrington continues to live and work in Berlin.

Cartoonists at risk

PLANTU, France

One cartoon can be more offensive than a thousand words. Recent articles by Joe Szabo in **Witty World** and Steve Platt in the **New Statesman** have catalogued a history of political fury, often about a single drawing, making the cartoonist the focus of much anger and often putting them in personal danger. In **Thin Black Lines** we featured the work of Naji al-Ali who was shot in London at the time we were compiling the book. Hanzala, the character who featured in many of his cartoons, despite "his" innocence upset a wide spectrum of political interests in the Middle East.

Joe Szabo writes - *"Since the birth of political cartooning, there has been resentment towards the genre and its cultivators. In the late 1800s, the American Thomas Nast's cartoons landed one corrupt New York politician in jail. Although Nast received many threats on his life, he actually suffered no physical harm. Not so, for a group of Polish cartoonists, who were executed on May 27th, 1944 for drawing against Nazi Fascism. Turkish cartoonist Sema Underger's cartoons were ripped off the wall and partially destroyed by fundamentalists, while Turhan Selcuk of the same country was tortured by the military junta there in 1970.*

Somehow, we got used to the fact that facing violence had been a calculated risk for courageous cartoonists in the past. Accepting the same in the 90s is much more difficult, but the cold fact is that cartoonists and their editors still get imprisoned, tortured and even killed today for doing their jobs."

Political fears about the potential influence of cartoons have prompted many attempts to restrict the activities of cartoonists. All too often this has involved infringing their human rights and threatened their personal safety. There have also been numerous attempts to restrict cartoonists, for example in Philadelphia legislation was introduced in 1903 banning caricatures of politicians; e.g. depicting them as animals. However, vegetables, which were not covered by the legislation, can be equally effective! - see **Thin Black Lines**.

In a section on stereotyping **Thin Black Lines** features ways in which cartooning can become part of the armoury of propaganda "dehumanising the enemy", for example during the Falklands War. Whatever our perspective we need to gain greater insight into why political cartoons are so effective and use them to generate awareness of contemporary issues.

The shape of the world

The cartoons in this first collection all feature the globe. They add to a similar collection in the original **Thin Black Lines**. They lend themselves to many of the activities suggested in the introduction but they also make a good starting point for an activity to get people to have a go at drawing their own cartoons. Less emphasis should be placed on artistic skill than on attempting to sum up a notion of how people see the world, or focus on a particular issue. Alternatively, people could work in groups to build up ideas . . . or perhaps to draw the world as they imagine it might be seen by someone else, for example different political leaders.

Some questions to help focus discussion:

- What words would you use to describe the global situations portrayed?

- What threats to the future do the cartoons highlight?

- Which threats to our common future do you think are the most serious?

HANEL, Germany

SKAUGE, Norway

EWK, Sweden

ARCADIO, Costa Rica

Thin Black Lines Rides Again

CUMMINGS, Canada

HAM, Finland

FIN DEL MUNDO (TEORIA)

TOM, Netherlands

SMIRNOV, Russia

ISAAC, Philippines

BAS, Greece

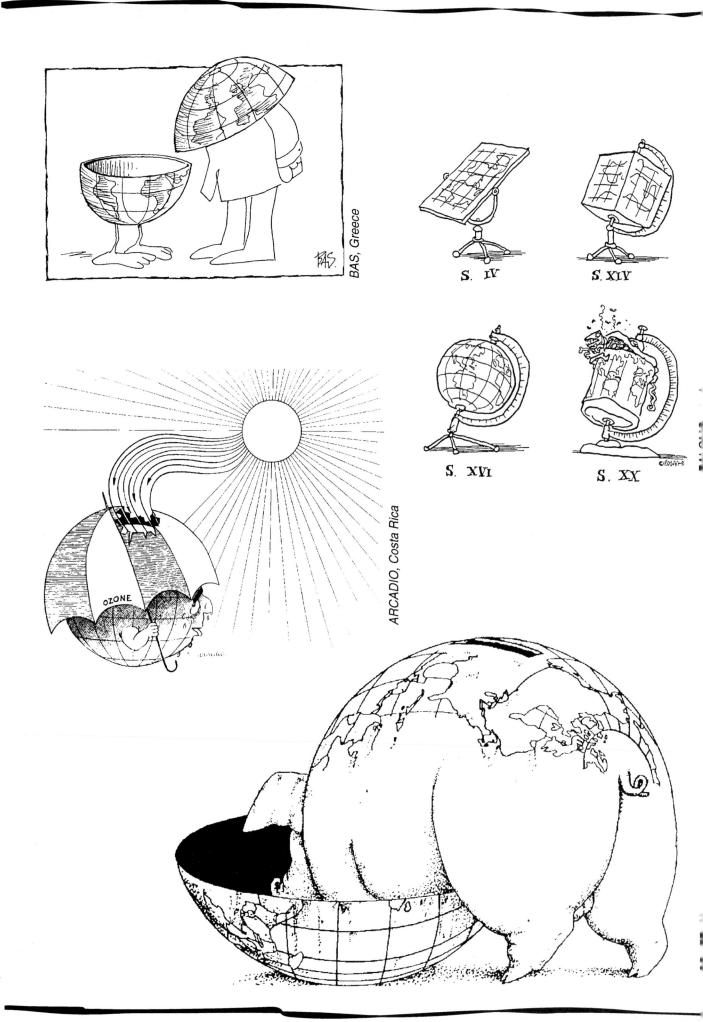

BAS, Greece

S. IV

S. XIV

S. XVI

S. XX

ARCADIO, Costa Rica

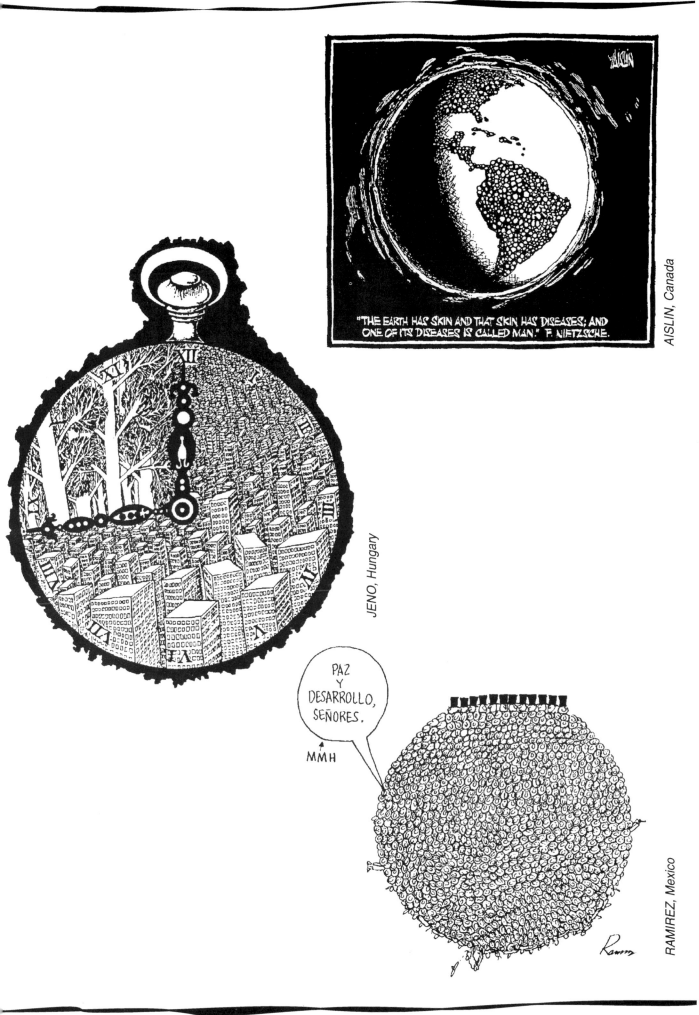

AISLIN, Canada

JENO, Hungary

RAMIREZ, Mexico

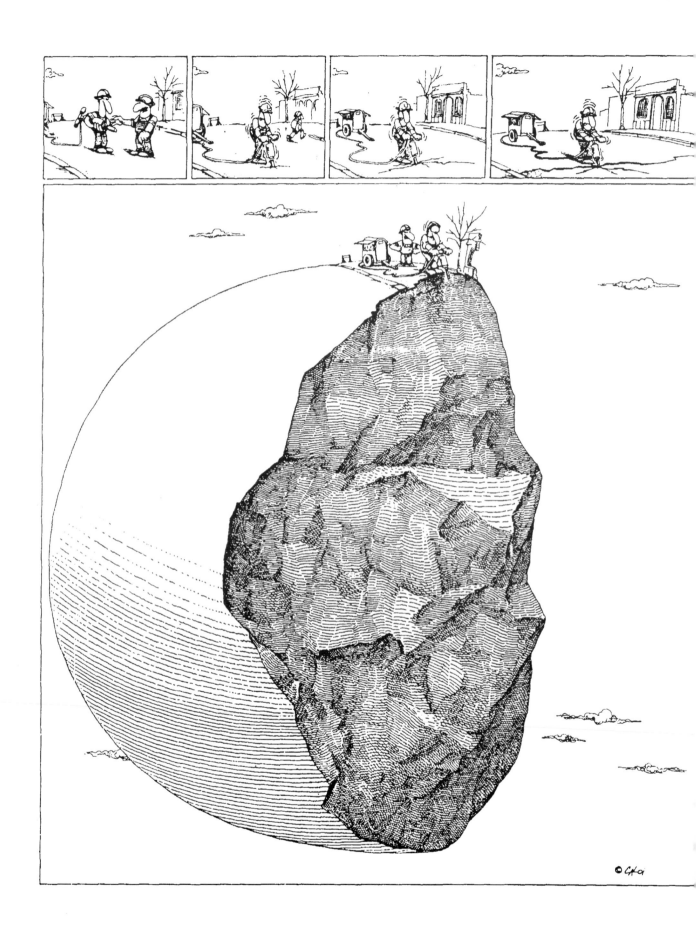

Human Rights

They invaded Kuwait, so we had no choice. Hussein had to be stopped, his record on human rights spoke for itself. Aristide was overthrown but things were not as simple in Haiti. What's happening in East Timor is appalling but diplomacy and persuasion must be used. And then there was [is?] Somalia, Bosnia, Northern Ireland . . . it's a good job we have our armies to protect our rights.

Human rights begins at breakfast . . . and continues with the dishes, the lunch, the dinner, the clothes line, job-sharing and equal opportunities.

Brazilian trade unionists continue to be assassinated alongside the street kids and the Indians; hunger continues amongst the poor in Africa and unemployment makes a mockery of being born free and equal but . . . the work of the Brazilian trade union movement, Amnesty International, public compassion and generosity and community support also continue.

TURNER, Ireland

Values ... the right to imagine

BAS, Greece

SMIRNOV, Russia

JOVANOVIC, Yugoslavia

STRELSOW, Russia

PETRICIC, Yugoslavia

ISBN 88-420 2797-9

ISBN 88-420-279

ISBN 88-420-2797 9

JEZEK, Italy

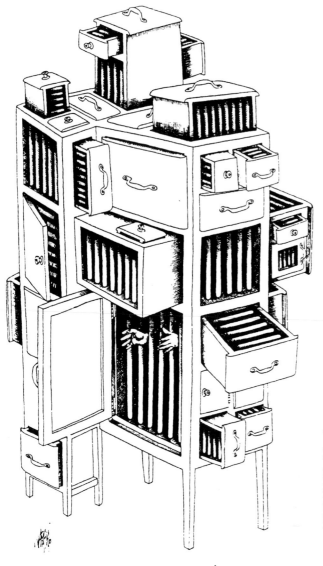

NARANJO, Mexico

JAVAD, Iran

JAVAD, Iran

MAXIMO, Spain

And are all treated equally?

20ᵀᴴ January 1994: The right of Sinn Fein/IRA to the airwaves....

......and the right of reply.......

WHAT'S **WRONG** WITH THOSE WIMPS IN THE MIDDLE EAST?!! ... DON'T THEY KNOW THAT PEOPLE'S **JOBS** ARE IN JEOPARDY?

ACME ARMS SALES

LEAHY, Australia

UNEMPLOYMENT

DE LA TORRE Q, Spain

I UNDERSTAND THEY'RE ENDANGERED, BUT WE'RE TALKING ABOUT JOBS.

P. Steiner
THE WASHINGTON TIMES

STEINER, USA

TAN, Turkey

THE JOB PICTURE

CUMMINGS, Canada

BALLESTA, Spain

STEINER, USA

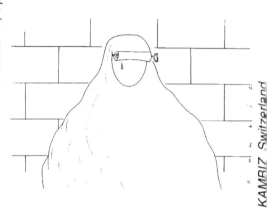

KAMBIZ, Switzerland

GABLE, Canada

AISLIN, Canada

AISLIN, Canada

PLANTU, France

TURGUT, Turkey

BAS, Greece

MOIR, Australia

SIGNE, USA

AISLIN, Canada

GOMAA, Egypt

KAL, USA

CHAPPATTE, Switzerland

34

CHILD ABUSE

ETHIOPIA 1988

KAL '87
Sunday Telegraph

Development Education Centre with Cartoonists & Writers Syndicate

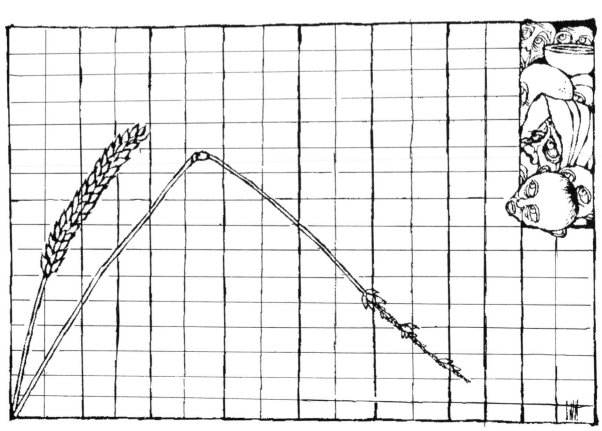

RAESIDE, Canada

EWK, Sweden

Responsibility ... pointing a finger?

TURNER, Ireland

Some questions to help focus discussion:

- *From amongst this collection of cartoons about human rights which do you like most/least? Explain your choice.*

- *According to these cartoonists, what are today's biggest threats to human rights?*

- *Make a list of the human rights issues highlighted by these cartoons.*

- *From your understanding of these cartoons, who is abusing whose rights?*

"AND WE USED TO ENTER INTO VAIN DISCOURSE WITH THOSE WHO ENTERED INTO VAIN DISCOURSE." KORAN: LXXIV-45

I SUPPOSE I CAN'T REALLY COMPLAIN— I'M ON A FREEBIE

MITCHELL, Australia

HOSTAGES

VEGETABLES

FROZEN

KHAKHANOW, Russia

McDONALD, Honduras

UN

BAS, Greece

KAL, USA

RAESIDE, Canada

SIGNE, USA

ARCADIO, Costa Rica

TURNER, Ireland

Environment

We are in a car, racing at 70 mph towards the edge of the cliff. Every bone in our body and every brain cell is screaming "Use the brakes, use the brakes". But the growth imperative is still seductively whispering in our ear "No, use the accelerator".*

Reports and conferences come and go. Forests, plants, animals, oceans, lakes, come and are gone. Each week New Yorkers use up as much energy in commuting as all Africans use in a whole year. Human needs get confused with human wants [to say nothing about human greed]. Green is the colour of the decade but brown is taking over our maps.

We may have fewer trees, less pure water, a gaping hole in the ozone layer, gross over consumption alongside horrific under consumption.................. but we still have our cartoonists.

[* Thanks are due to Fr Sean McDonagh for this comment.]

KAZANEVSKY, Ukraine

V. KAZANEVSKY

In words ... and deeds

BAS, Greece

BAS
TACHYDROMOS
Athens
GREECE

BAS, Greece

BAS, Greece

RIO DE JANEIRO

BAS, Greece

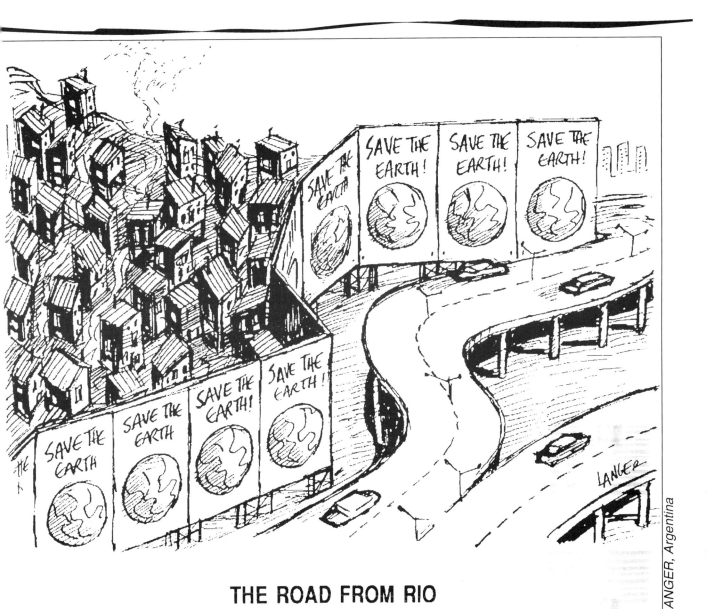

THE ROAD FROM RIO

LANGER, Argentina

SKAUGE, Norway

ARCADIO, Costa Rica

Thin Black Lines Rides Again

BOERGER, Japan

Some questions to help focus discussion:

- *What threats to the environment do the cartoons highlight?*

- *Make a list of the cartoons in this section which raise issues which involve: 1] you, 2] the government, 3] business people and 4] international organisations.*

- *Draw your own environmental issues cartoon.*

TAKE EVERYTHING AS YOU CAN... A TERRIBLE CRISIS IS COMING!

LANGER, Argentina

DE ANGELIS, Italy

Thin Black Lines Rides Again

INDUSTRIALIZED COUNTRIES

McDONALD, Honduras

Not even the trees . . . ?

SIGNE, USA

MENA, Spain

JAVAD, Iran

DE ANGELIS, Italy

ARCADIO, Costa Rica

. . . Nor the sea . . . ?

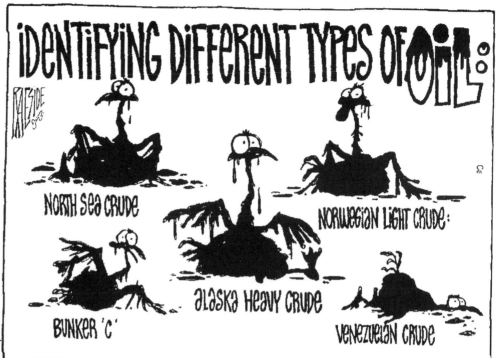

Nor the air?

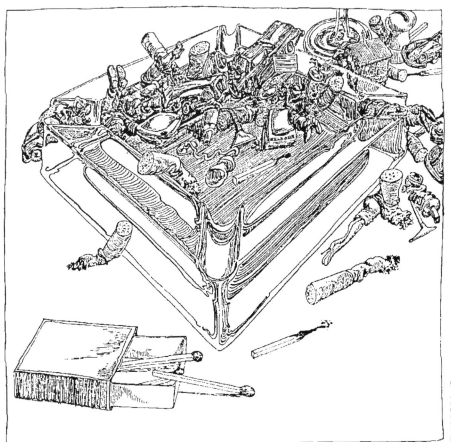

RAUCH, Germany

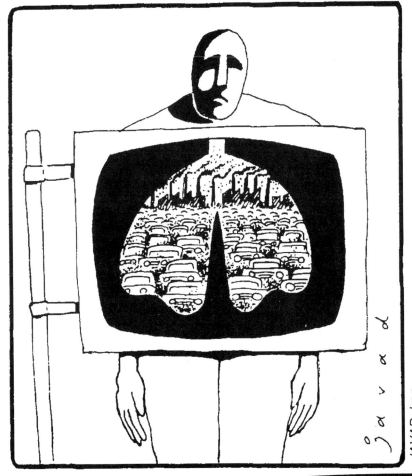

JAVAD, Iran

EWK, Sweden

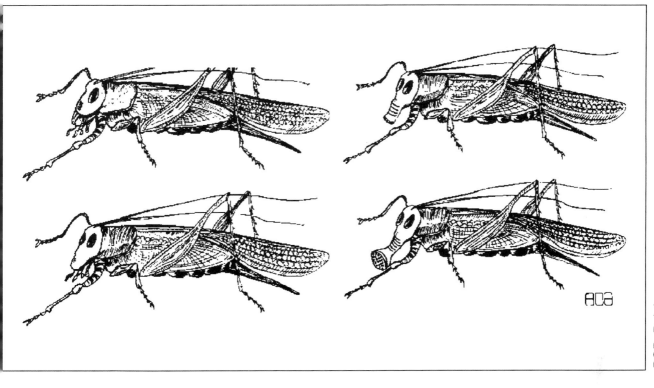

BOB, Belgium

MENA, Spain

CUMMINGS, Canada

RAESIDE, Canada

KAL, USA

EWK, Sweden

Now we know . . . or do we?

Hands up those who would believe a report that says there is little evidence that Chernobyl has damaged health...

TURNER Northern Ireland

NUCLEAR WASTE DISPOSAL

TROG England

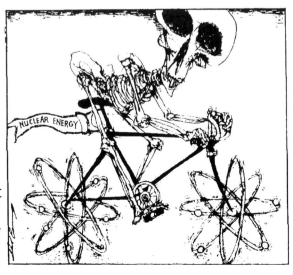

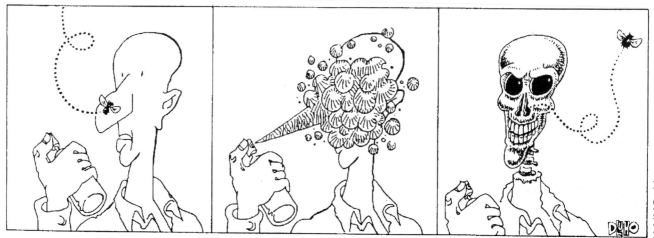

The end of an era?

Some people even went so far as to claim that it was the "end of history" as we had known it. With the collapse of communism and the apparent triumph of capitalism worldwide, the world had been turned upside down and we were now facing a whole new order of things.

Curiously, in many parts of Africa, Latin America and Asia, as well as amongst many groups and regions in the industrial world, the message did not seem to have gotten through. Things went on much as they had before [and still do today] - wealth flowed from poor to rich; power did not get redistributed; poverty grew and the struggle for human dignity continued apace.

The New World Order appeared to be a lot like the old world order and, despite the loss of an odd leader or two, **they** appeared to remain in control.

But maybe we just expect too much....!

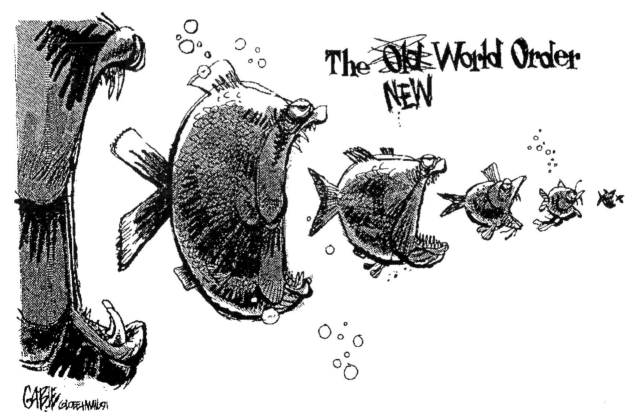

The ~~Old~~ NEW World Order

GABLE, Canada

New world order . . . out of order

NEW WORLD ORDER

OLD WORLD ORDER

KEY
GOOD
EVIL

KEY
OK | NOT-SO-HOT | BAD | WORSE | EVEN WORSE | WRECKED | UN-SPEAK-ABLE

SIGNE, USA

WARMING UP FOR 1993

RELIGIOUS FUNDAMENTALISTS
SERBS
KHMER ROUGE

HENG, Singapore

„Kleidungswechsel"

1.
2.
NATIONALISMUS

AMMER, Austria

WHRRRRR
WHRRRRR
SNAP
WHRRRR
CLICK
CLICK WHRR
CLICK

POST-RUSSIAN ROULETTE

KIRSCHEN, Isreal

AMMER, Austria

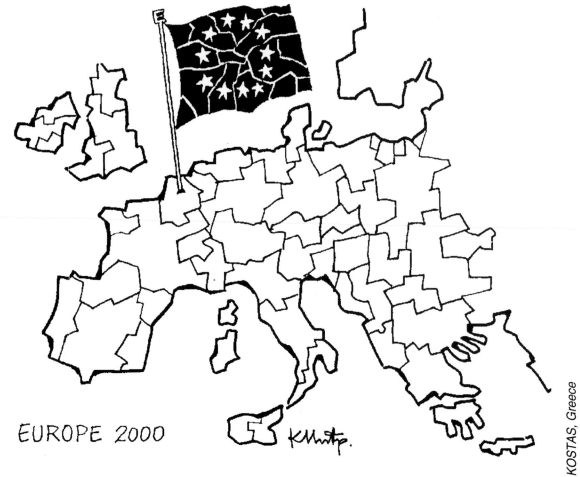

EUROPE 2000

KOSTAS, Greece

Thin Black Lines Rides Again

GABLE, Canada

GABLE, Canada

TOM, Netherlands

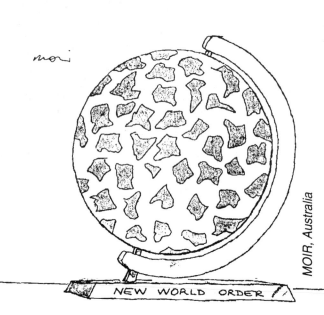

NEW WORLD ORDER

MOIR, Australia

HELLO! NEW WORLD ORDER HERE!

PANCHO

PANCHO, France

NEW WORLD ORDER

MOIR, Australia

SKAUGE, Norway

JOVANOVIC, Yugoslavia

PLANTU, France

McDONALD, Honduras

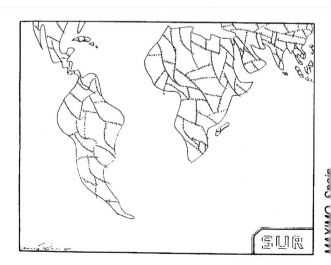

Thin Black Lines Rides Aga[...]

CALDERON, Mexico

HENG, Singapore

AMMER, Austria

ARCADIO, Costa Rica

McDonalds in Moscow

McDONALD, Honduras

LANGER

PALOMO, Mexico

Thin Black Lines Rides Again

TOM, Netherlands

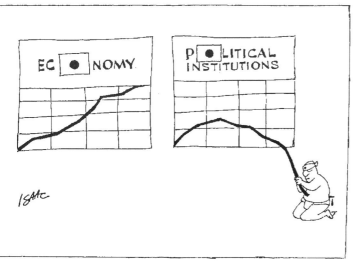

ISAAC, Philippines

ARCADIO, Costa Rica

HENG, Singapore

PURI
THE STATESMAN
New Delhi
INDIA

PURI, India

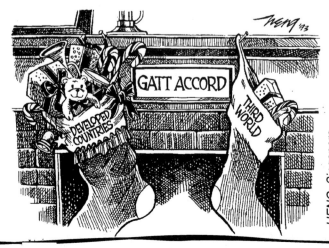

HENG, Singapore

Thin Black Lines Rides Again

MOCHALOV, Russia

MOCHALOV, Russia

MOCHALOV, Russia

ARCADIO, Costa Rica

ARCADIO, Costa Rica

Thin Black Lines Rides Again

Debt . . . paying with their lives?

SOUVENIRS —

CUMMINGS, Canada

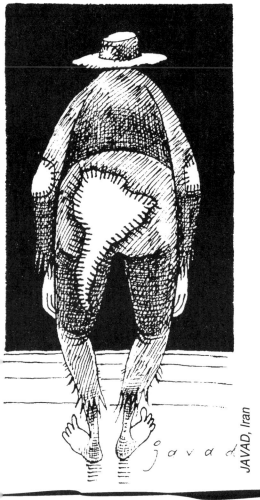

JAVAD, Iran

PLANTU, France

They're deciding whether or not to shout for help!

OGUNBADEJO, Nigeria

NICOLIELO, Brazil

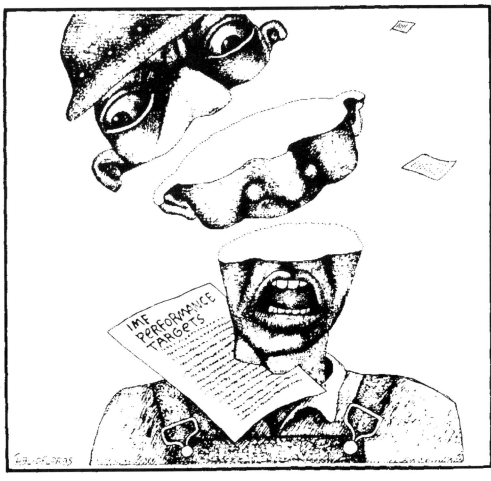

HELIOFLORES, Mexico

BANEGAS, Honduras

McDONALD, Honduras

Arms . . . winners . . . and losers

1991: Germans help arm the Gulf....

1993: The Gulf reciprocates...

TURNER, Ireland

DISGUSTING ....

CUMMINGS
CANADA

CUMMINGS, Canada

BEHRENDT, Netherlands

NARANJO, Mexico

NARANJO, Mexico

NARANJO, Mexico

BOB, Belgium

TURGUT, Turkey

MITCHELL, Australia

HEY..!

IF ALL THE GUNS AND TANKS AND MISSILES MADE REDUNDANT BY THE FINISH OF THE COLD WAR....

..WERE LAID END TO END......

..IT WOULD MAKE THEM A LOT EASIER TO SELL TO DEVELOPING NATIONS.....

CLOSING DOWN SALE

MUST CLEAR   BARGAINS

TURNER, Ireland

Conflict . . . war no more?

Some questions to help focus discussion:

- Identify the issues/places shown in these cartoons.

- What are the similarities /dissimilarities between the "old" and "new" world orders as shown in the cartoons?

- Who do you think are the "winners" and the "losers"?

- In your opinion, do the cartoonists show today's most important issues?

Thin Black Lines Rides Again

BEHRENDT, Netherlands

KAL, USA

NO-FLY ZONE

GABLE, Canada

SADDAM

Pollution in the Gulf

OMAR, Egypt

BAS, Greece

KAL, USA

SOUTH AFRICA'S BACK IN THE OLYMPICS....

TURNER, Ireland

ARCADIO
LA NACION
San Jose
COSTA RICA

RACIAL BARRIERS

INKHATA

AFRICAN NATIONAL CONGRESS

SOUTH AFRICA

arcadio

ARCADIO, Costa Rica

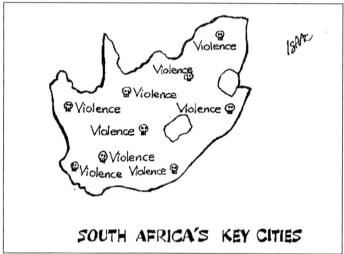

SOUTH AFRICA'S KEY CITIES

ISAAC, Philippines

BLUSTER'S LAST STAND

SOUTH AFRICAN MEMORIAL

FEDLER, South Africa

Will democracy extinguish it?

TAYO, Nigeria

AMMER, Austria

ARCADIO, Costa Rica

FEDLER, South Africa

The future UN role . . . a UNited future?

TURNER, Ireland

MITCHELL, Australia

Thin Black Lines Rides Again

RAESIDE, Canada

PLANTU, France

EVOLUTION

GABLE, Canada

MOIR, Australia

MOIR, Australia

MOIR, Australia

MOIR, Australia

HANEL, Germany

HANEL, Germany

TOMASCHOFF, Germany

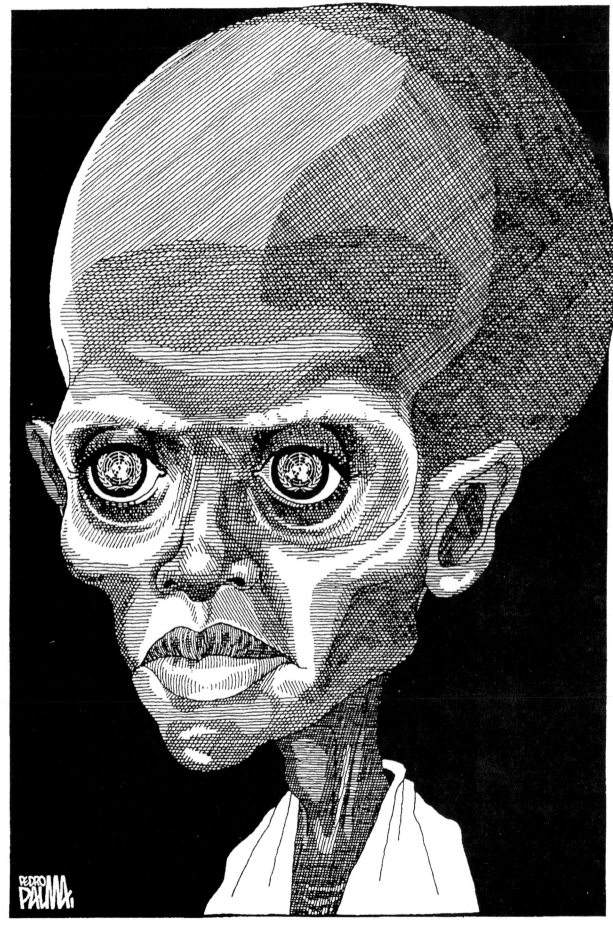

PALMA. Portugal

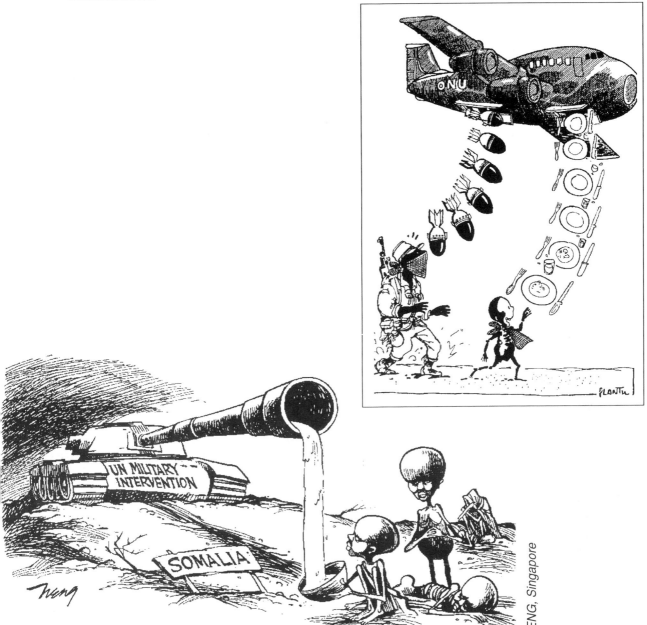

PLANTU, France

HENG, Singapore

TURNER, Ireland

TURNER, Ireland

HENG, Singapore

TURNER, Ireland

Index of Cartoonists

AISLIN	19, 29*, 31, 38
AL ALI	14
AMMER	65, 66, 71, 91
ARCADIO	16, 18, 41, 45, 51, 53, 71, 73, 76*, 86, 90, 91
BALLESTA	28
BANEGAS	79
BAS	17, 18, 22, 30, 40, 44*, 64, 89
BATELLIER	38
BEHRENDT	81, 85
BOB	57, 83
BOERGER	46
CALDERON	71
CALOI	20
CESC	48
CHAPPATTE	33, 46
CHEREPANOV	70
CUMMINGS	17, 27, 47*, 58, 61, 77, 81
DE ANGELIS	48, 51
DE LA TORRE Q	27
DLUHO	62
EWK	16, 36, 50, 56, 59, 61
FEDLER	90, 91
GABLE	26, 28, 53, 63, 64, 67*, 87, 93
GOMAA	33
GRAFF	18
HAGEN	54
HAM	17
HANEL	15, 95*
HARRINGTON	8-13*
HELIOFLORES	79
HENG	65, 71, 74*, 97, 98
ISAAC	17, 61, 73, 90
JAVAD	25*, 51, 55, 77
JENO	19
JEZEK	24
JOVANOVIC	23, 69
KAL	33, 35, 40, 59, 70, 84, 85, 89
KAMBIZ	28
KAZANEVSKY	43
KHAKHANOW	39
KIRSCHEN	65
KOSTAS	66
LANGER	5, 45, 48, 53, 72
LEAHY	27
LIPINSKI	62
MAXIMO	25, 70
McDONALD	39, 49, 70, 72, 79, 86
MENA	51, 57
MITCHELL	34, 38, 78, 83, 92
MOCHALOV	75*
MOIR	30, 34, 40, 68*, 94*
NARANJO	4, 5, 24, 78, 82*
NICOLIELO	78
OGUNBADEJO	78
OMAR	87
PALMA	96
PALOMO	18, 47, 53, 72
PANCHO	68
PETRICIC	23
PLANTU	14, 29, 70, 77, 93, 97
PURI	74
RAESIDE	36, 41, 52*, 58*, 93
RAMIREZ	19
RAUCH	55
SERGUEI	61
SIGNE	7, 30, 32*, 41, 51, 65
SKAUGE	16, 45, 54, 69
SMIRNOV	17, 22, 80
STEINER	27, 28
STRELSOW	23
TAN	27
TAYO	91
TESLER	24
TOM	17, 35, 50, 68, 73, 88
TOMASCHOFF	95
TROG	60
TURGUT	29, 83
TURNER	21, 26, 37, 42, 60, 81, 83, 88, 89, 92, 97, 98*
ZLATKOVSKY	22, 35

[* More than one cartoon on that page]

Acknowledgements

We would like to thank the following cartoonists and their newspapers:

AISLIN, The Gazette, Montreal, Canada
AL ALI, Lebanon
AMMER, Weiner Zeitung, Vienna, Austria
ARCADIO, La Nacion and The Tico Times, San Jose, Costa Rica
BALLESTA, Madrid, Spain
BANEGAS, La Prensa, San Pedro Paul, Honduras
BAS, Tachydromos, Athens, Greece
BATELLIER, Le Matin, Paris, France
BEHRENDT, Netherlands
BOB, Het Nieuwsblad, Brussels, Belgium
BOERGER, The Daily Yomiuri, Tokyo, Japan
CALDERON, El Norte, Nuevo Leon, Mexico
CALOI, Buenos Aires, Argentina
CESC, Barcelona, Spain
CHAPPATTE, L'Hebdo and La Suisse, Geneva, Switzerland
CHEREPANOV, Krokodil, Moscow, Russia
CUMMINGS, Winnipeg Free Press, Winnipeg, Canada
DE ANGELIS, Il Popolo, Rome, Italy
DE LA TORRE Q, Ya, Madrid, Spain
DLUHO, Nepszava, Budapest, Hungary
EWK, Aftonbladet, Stockholm, Sweden
FEDLER, The Star, Johannesburg, South Africa
GABLE, Globe and Mail, Toronto, Canada
GOMAA, Al Alam Al Youm, Cairo, Egypt
GRAFF, Dagbladet, Oslo, Norway
HAGEN, Verdens Gang, Oslo, Norway
HAM, Espoo, Finland
HANEL, Frankfurter Allgemeine, Frankfurt, Germany
HELIOFLORES, El Universal, Mexico City, Mexico
HENG, Lianhe Zaobao, Singapore, Singapore
ISAAC, Bulletin Today, Manila, Philippines
JAVAD, Abrar and Tanz-O-Caricature, Tehran, Iran
JENO, Hungary
JEZEK, Italy
JOVANOVIC, Komunist, Belgrade, [Yugoslavia]
KAL, Baltimore Sun, Baltimore, USA
KAMBIZ, Nebelspalter, Basel, Switzerland
KAZANEVSKY, Ukraine
KHAKHANOW, Russia
KIRSCHEN, The Jerusalem Report, Jerusalem, Israel
KOSTAS, Ta Nea, Athens, Greece
LANGER, Humor, Buenos Aires, Argentina
LEAHY, Courier-Mail, Brisbane, Australia
LIPINSKI, Szpilki, Warsaw, Poland
MAXIMO, El Pais, Madrid, Spain
McDONALD, Diario El Heraldo, San Pedro Sula, Honduras